WILMETTE PUBLIC LIBRARY

3 1239 00577 0398

D1222519

WITHDRAWN
Wilmette Public Library

WILMETTE PUBLIC LIBRARY
1242 WILMETTE AVENUE
WILMETTE, IL 60091
847-256-5025

THE LAST FLOWER

A PARABLE IN PICTURES

WILMETTE PUBLIC LIBRARY

THE LAST FLOWER

A PARABLE IN PICTURES

By

James Thurber

HARPER & BROTHERS · PUBLISHERS · NEW YORK · AND · LONDON · 1939

Copyright, 1939, by James Thurber
Printed in the United States of America
All rights in this book are reserved.
No part of the book may be reproduced
in any manner whatsoever without
written permission. For information
address Harper & Brothers

11 - 39

BOMC offers recordings and compact discs, cassettes
and records. For information and catalog write to
BOMR, Camp Hill, PA 17012.

741.5973
TH

FOR ROSEMARY

IN THE WISTFUL HOPE THAT HER WORLD
WILL BE BETTER THAN MINE

THE LAST FLOWER

A PARABLE IN PICTURES

WORLD WAR XII, AS EVERYBODY KNOWS,

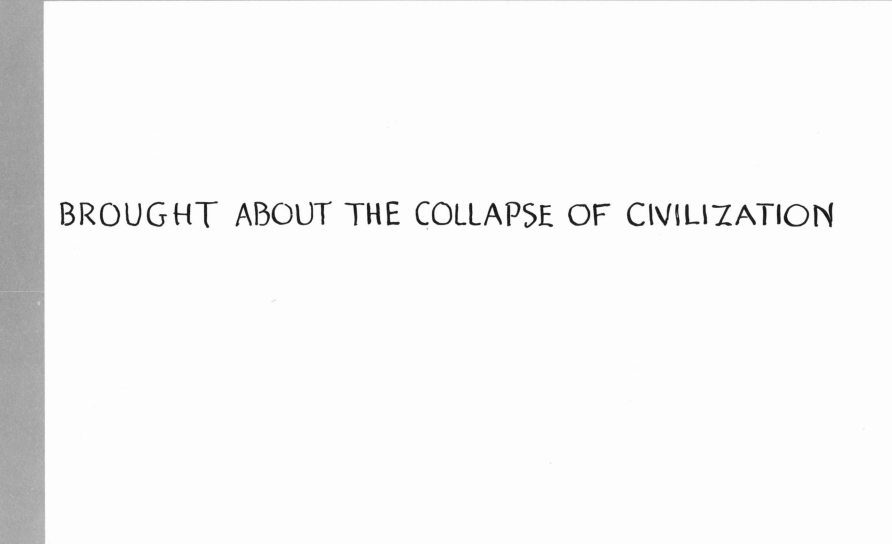

BROUGHT ABOUT THE COLLAPSE OF CIVILIZATION

TOWNS, CITIES, AND VILLAGES DISAPPEARED

FROM THE EARTH

ALL THE GROVES AND FORESTS WERE
DESTROYED

AND ALL THE GARDENS

AND ALL THE WORKS OF ART

MEN, WOMEN, AND CHILDREN BECAME LOWER
THAN THE LOWER ANIMALS

DISCOURAGED AND DISILLUSIONED, DOGS DESERTED

THEIR FALLEN MASTERS

EMBOLDENED BY THE PITIFUL CONDITION
OF THE FORMER LORDS OF THE EARTH,
RABBITS DESCENDED UPON THEM

BOOKS, PAINTINGS, AND MUSIC DISAPPEARED
FROM THE EARTH, AND HUMAN BEINGS
JUST SAT AROUND, DOING NOTHING

YEARS AND YEARS WENT BY

EVEN THE FEW GENERALS WHO WERE LEFT
FORGOT WHAT THE LAST WAR HAD DECIDED

BOYS AND GIRLS GREW UP TO STARE AT EACH OTHER BLANKLY, FOR LOVE HAD PASSED FROM THE EARTH

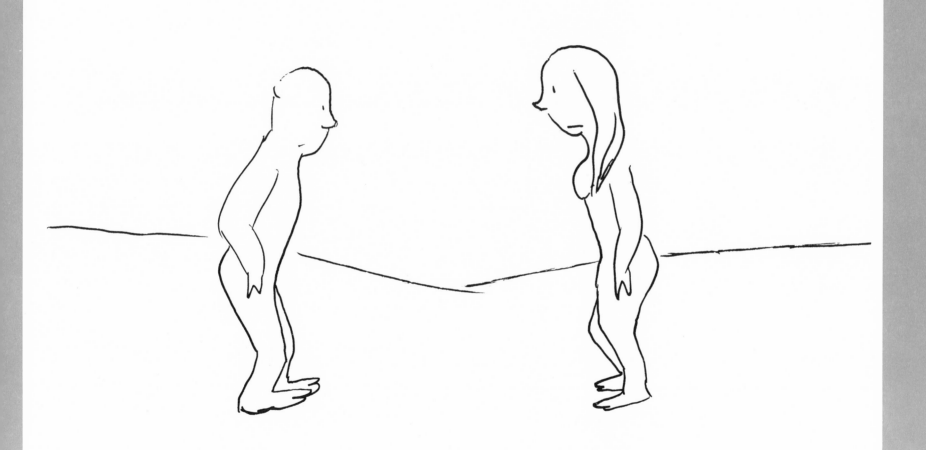

ONE DAY A YOUNG GIRL WHO HAD NEVER
SEEN A FLOWER CHANCED TO COME
UPON THE LAST ONE IN THE WORLD

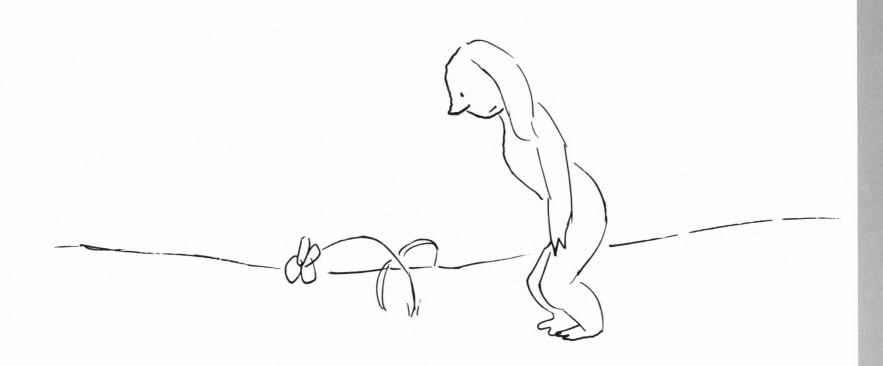

SHE TOLD THE OTHER HUMAN BEINGS
THAT THE LAST FLOWER WAS DYING

THE ONLY ONE WHO PAID ANY ATTENTION
TO HER WAS A YOUNG MAN SHE
FOUND WANDERING ABOUT

TOGETHER THE YOUNG MAN AND THE GIRL
NURTURED THE FLOWER AND IT BEGAN
TO LIVE AGAIN

ONE DAY A BEE VISITED THE FLOWER,
AND A HUMMINGBIRD

BEFORE LONG THERE WERE TWO FLOWERS, AND
THEN FOUR, AND THEN A GREAT MANY

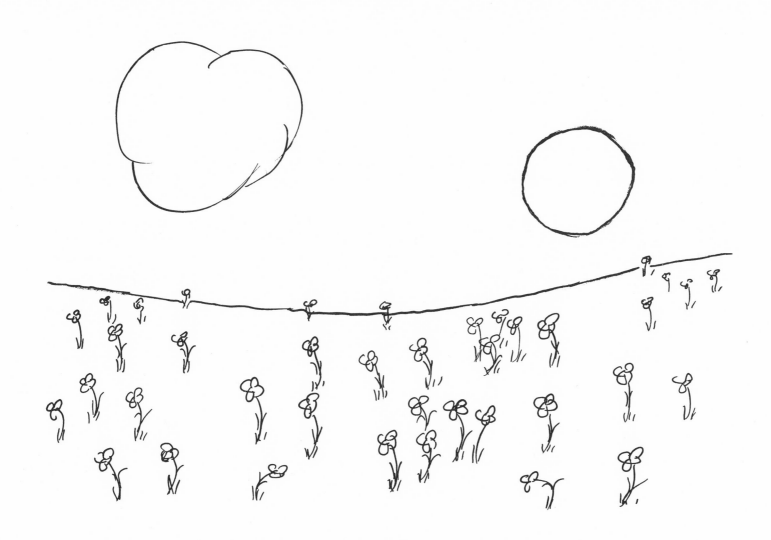

GROVES AND FORESTS FLOURISHED AGAIN

THE YOUNG GIRL BEGAN TO TAKE
AN INTEREST IN HOW SHE LOOKED

THE YOUNG MAN DISCOVERED THAT
TOUCHING THE GIRL WAS PLEASURABLE

LOVE WAS REBORN INTO THE WORLD

THEIR CHILDREN GREW UP STRONG AND HEALTHY
AND LEARNED TO RUN AND LAUGH

DOGS CAME OUT OF THEIR EXILE

THE YOUNG MAN DISCOVERED, BY PUTTING ONE STONE UPON ANOTHER, HOW TO BUILD A SHELTER

PRETTY SOON EVERYBODY WAS BUILDING SHELTERS

TOWNS, CITIES, AND VILLAGES SPRANG UP

SONG CAME BACK INTO THE WORLD

AND TROUBADOURS AND JUGGLERS

AND TAILORS AND COBBLERS

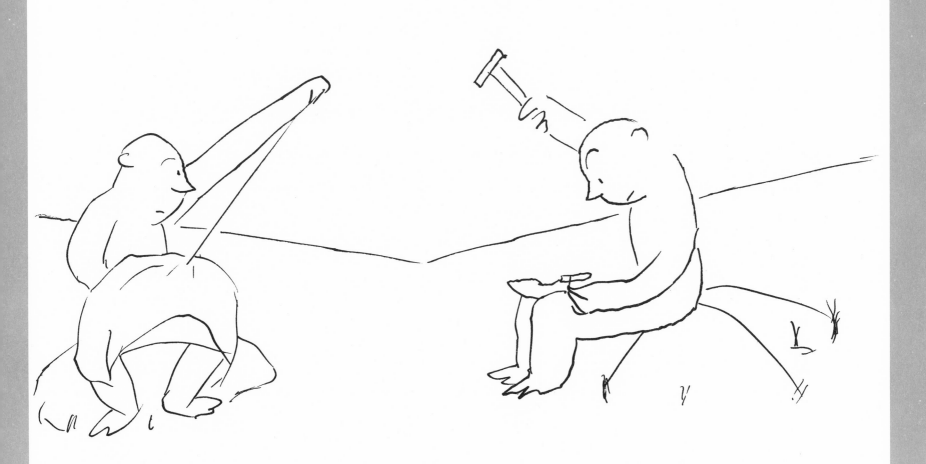

AND PAINTERS AND POETS

AND SCULPTORS AND WHEELWRIGHTS

AND SOLDIERS

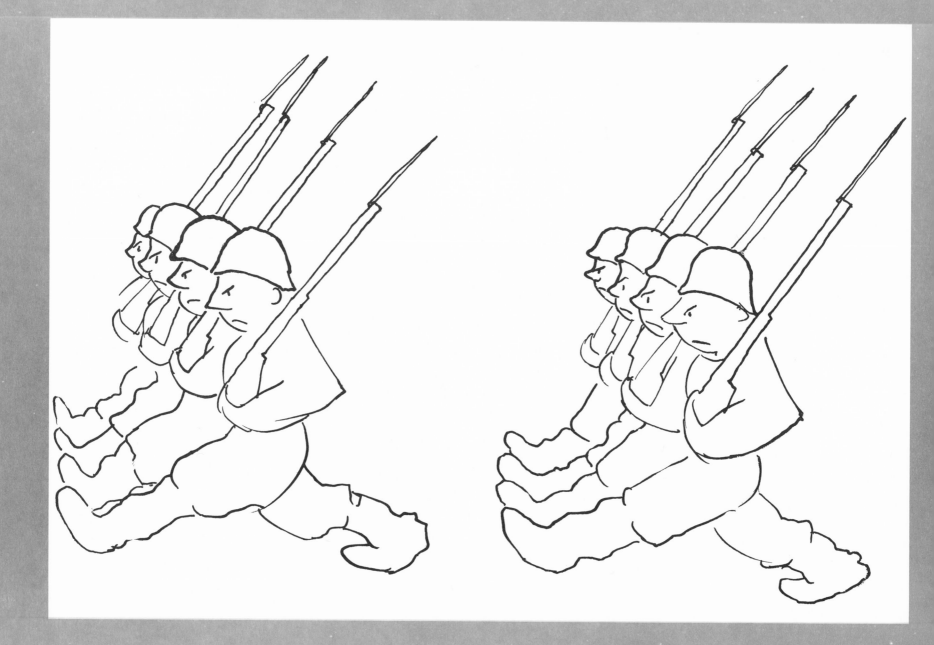

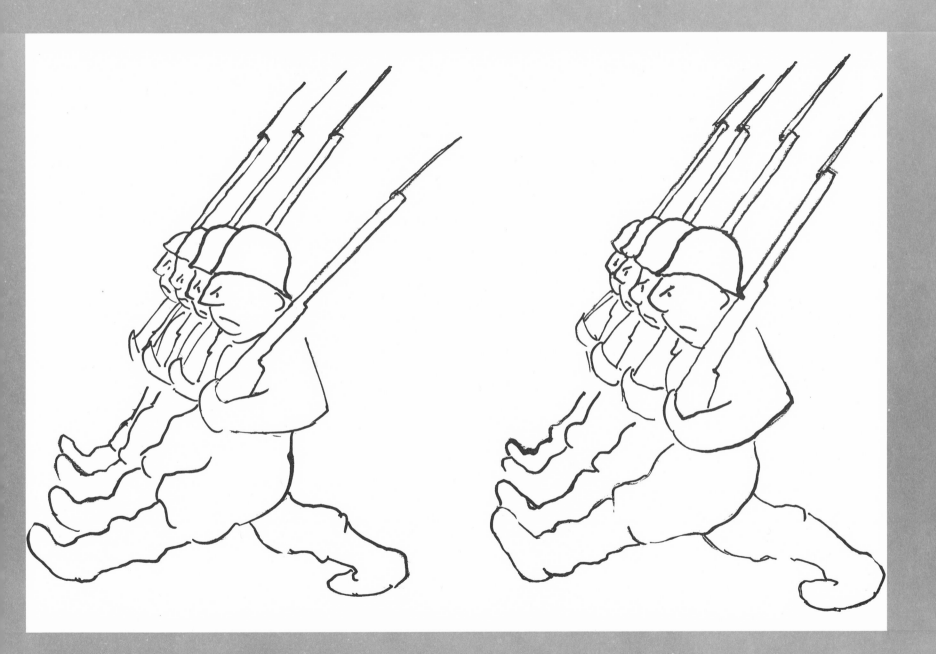

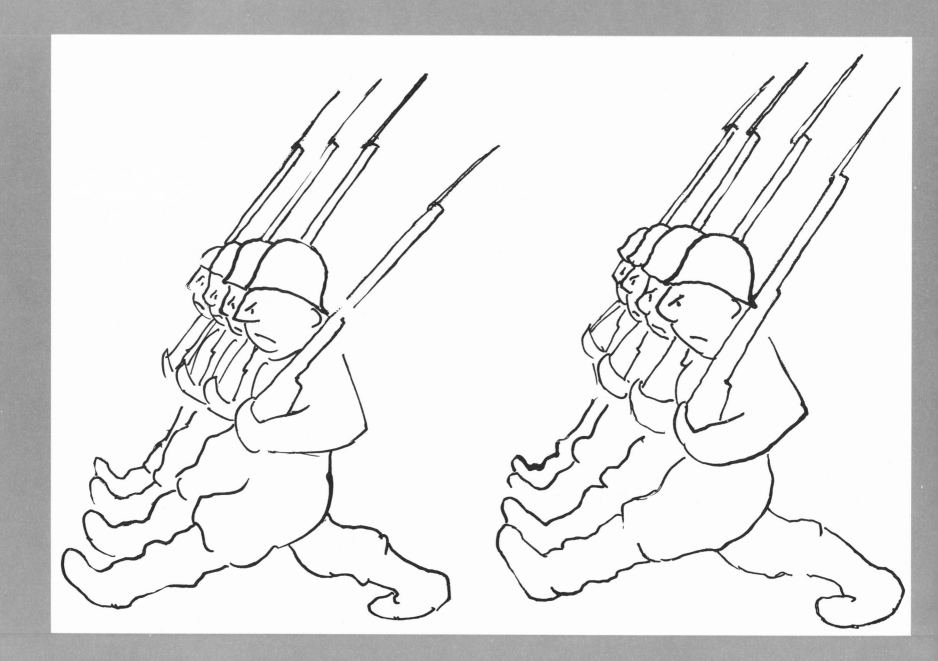

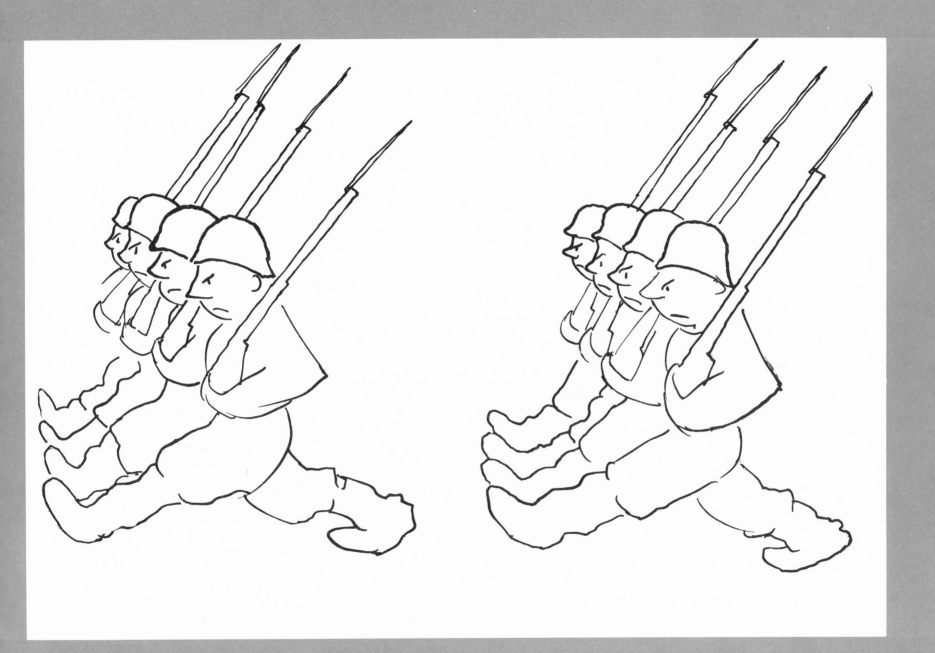

AND LIEUTENANTS AND CAPTAINS

AND GENERALS AND MAJOR-GENERALS

AND LIBERATORS

SOME PEOPLE WENT ONE PLACE TO LIVE,
AND SOME ANOTHER

BEFORE LONG, THOSE WHO WENT TO LIVE IN THE VALLEYS
WISHED THEY HAD GONE TO LIVE IN THE HILLS

AND THOSE WHO HAD GONE TO LIVE IN THE HILLS

WISHED THEY HAD GONE TO LIVE IN THE VALLEYS

THE LIBERATORS, UNDER THE GUIDANCE OF GOD,
SET FIRE TO THE DISCONTENT

SO PRESENTLY THE WORLD WAS AT WAR AGAIN

THIS TIME THE DESTRUCTION WAS SO COMPLETE...

THAT NOTHING AT ALL WAS LEFT IN THE WORLD

EXCEPT ONE MAN

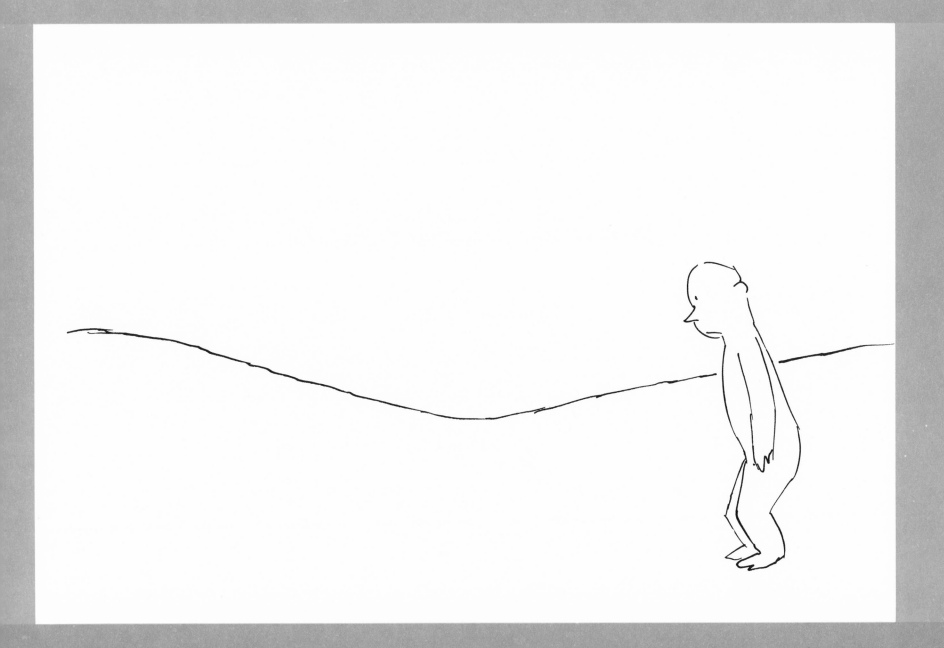

AND ONE WOMAN

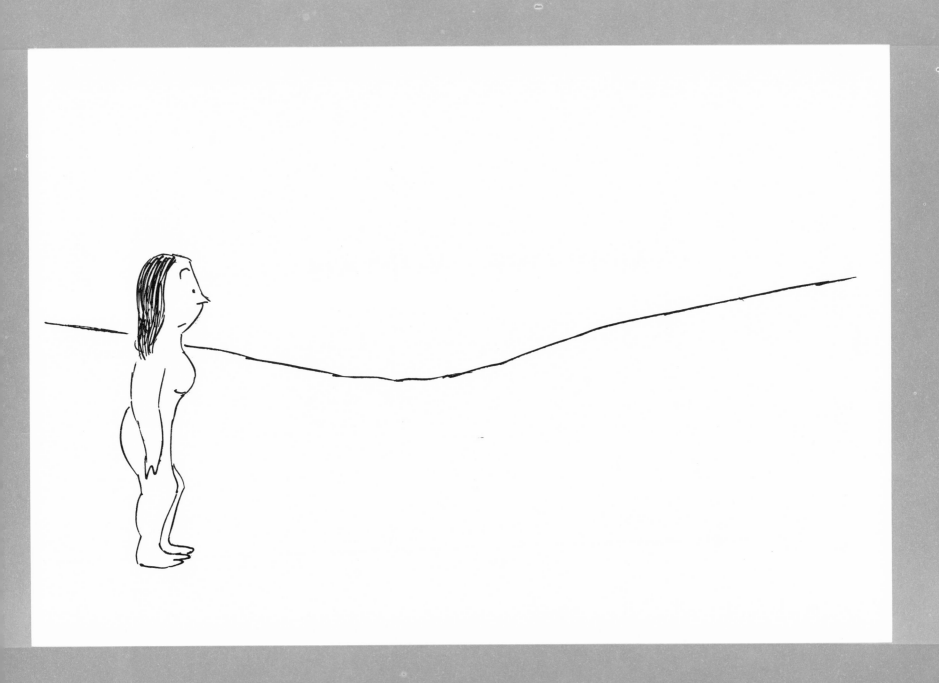

AND ONE FLOWER

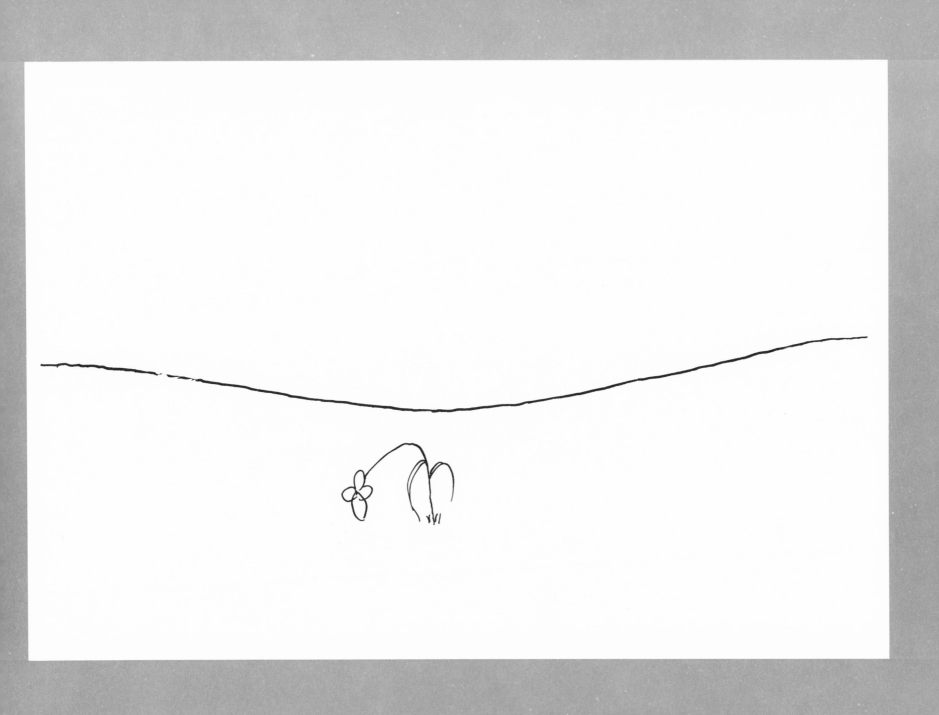